Pat-a-Cake

AND MORE PLAY-ALONG RHYMES

Illustrated by
KRISTA BRAUCKMANN-TOWNS
JANE CHAMBLESS WRIGHT
WENDY EDELSON
ANITA NELSON
LORI NELSON FIELD
DEBBIE PINKNEY
KAREN PRITCHETT

PUBLICATIONS INTERNATIONAL, LTD.

PAT-A-CAKE

Pat-a-cake, pat-a-cake,
    Baker's man!
Bake me a cake
    As fast as you can.
Pat it, and prick it,
    And mark it with a *B.*
Put it in the oven
    For Baby and me.

Rain, Rain, Go Away

Rain, rain, go away,
    Come again another day;
Little Johnny wants to play.

A Sure Test

If you are to be a gentleman,
  As I suppose you'll be,
You'll neither laugh nor smile
  For a tickling of the knee.

HERE SITS THE LORD MAYOR

Here sits the Lord Mayor.
    Here sit his two men.
Here sits the cock.
    Here sits the hen.
Here sit the little chickens.
    Here they run in.

Come Out to Play

Girls and boys,
　　Come out to play.
The moon doth shine
　　As bright as day.
Leave your supper,
　　And leave your sleep,
And come play with
　　　your playfellows
Into the street.

MULBERRY BUSH

Here we go round the mulberry bush,
  The mulberry bush, the mulberry bush
Here we go round the mulberry bush,
  On a cold and frosty morning.

BILLY, BILLY

Billy, Billy, come and play,
    While the sun shines bright as day.
Yes, my Polly, so I will,
    For I love to please you still.
Billy, Billy, have you seen

Sam and Betsy on the green?
Yes, my dear I saw them pass,
  Skipping over the new-mown grass.
Billy, Billy, come along,
  And I will sing a pretty song.

LITTLE JUMPING JOAN

Here I am,
Little Jumping Joan.
When nobody's with me,
I'm all alone.

THIS LITTLE PIGGY

This little piggy went to market.
   This little piggy stayed home.
This little piggy had roast beef.
   This little piggy had none.
This little piggy cried,
   "Wee-wee-wee,"
All the way home.

SWIM

Mother, may I go out to swim?
   Yes, my darling daughter.
Hang your clothes on a hickory limb
   And don't go near the water.